My name is

____

I am__________years old

I love my **Mango** Book

First Published March 2009

Book Design
Design Difference, Kochi

Printed in India
Standard Press Pvt. Ltd., Sivakasi

Publisher
DC Books
21/3 Shrungar Complex, M G Road, Bangalore, Karnataka, India
D C Kizhakemuri Edam, Good Shepherd Street, Kottayam 686 001, Kerala, India
Website: www.tumbi.org
Email: editorial@tumbi.org

ISBN 978-81-264-2295-1
MANGO 0039

DC Books: The first Indian Book Publishing House to get ISO Certification

MULLAH NASRUDDIN

WORSHIPPING A NAIL

RETOLD BY **SHWETHA E GEORGE**
ILLUSTRATED BY **PRASENJIT SANYAL**

Mullah Nasruddin was a kind hearted man. He gave generously to the poor and soon had no money left. He was forced to borrow money from his friends for his daily needs. Eventually his debts grew and the Mullah had to find a way to repay his loans. All that was left with him was his ancestral home, so he decided to sell it. Nasruddin's neighbour, Ali, was a cunning man who knew all about Nasruddin's difficulties so he thought to himself, "This is the perfect time to make some money out of Nasruddin."

Ali went to Nasruddin's house and stroking his large, bushy moustache said, "I heard you have no money to repay your debts. I want to help you, good neighbour. So, I will buy your house even though I don't have any interest in it."

But Ali offered a low price for the house. Nasruddin was disappointed but he had no choice and agreed to sell the house to Ali.

"God bless you with long life and healthy sons for this generous gesture!" said Nasruddin and drew a small piece of paper from the folds of his clothing. "The house shall be yours, as soon as we take care of this little clause in the contract." Ali grew suspicious. "What clause?"

"Oh, it's only a small thing," said Nasruddin. "This house was built by my father."

"A fine gentleman he was. Always paid in cash," remarked Ali.

"Yes. And you see here on the wall of this room," said Nasruddin, "there is one nail sticking out. My father never had the chance to finish hammering it in. He died before that."

"God bless his soul!" said Ali.

"I therefore request that I be allowed to keep ownership of the nail, and do whatever I want with it," said Nasruddin.

Ali thought to himself, "That is a very harmless thing. Let the poor man worship it."

He agreed to Nasruddin's wish but explained that he would have to consult his wife.

But Ali's wife was not happy on hearing this suggestion. "Why does he want to keep a nail?"

Ali tried to soothe her. "He just wants to 'worship' his nail from time to time. That is all," he said.

"He is crazy!"

"Maybe," said Ali, "but we are getting the house for half its value. We would be fools to let such an opportunity slip away all because of a nail!"

Ali's wife finally relented, the contract was signed, and Nasruddin moved out.

A month went by. One evening Ali heard a knock on the door. It was Nasruddin.

"Oh Mullah, where have you been? We were wondering about you," said Ali pretending to be happy on seeing the Mullah. Nasruddin explained that he had come to worship his nail.

Ali let him into the house.

Nasruddin bowed before the nail, removed his hat and put it on the nail.

As he was about to leave, Ali asked, "Hey, hey, what is that doing there?"

"That is my hat," said Nasruddin.

"Yes, but you cannot leave it in my house," said Ali.

"Of course, I can," said Nasruddin, as he headed towards the door, "it is on my nail."

Two weeks passed before Nasruddin's next visit.

"Ah, good morning Mullah," said Ali. "You have come to take back your hat, I presume."

"No, my dear friend, I have come to worship my nail."

Once again, he bowed before the nail and, after his prayers, he hung a scarf with his hat on the nail.

Ali was not amused but there was nothing he could do. He told himself that this could be Nasruddin's last visit because there was nothing more he could possibly hang on the nail. He slammed the door behind the departing Nasruddin and hoped his wife would not be too angry.

But a week later, Nasruddin returned. He bowed before the nail and before turning to leave, he took off his coat and hung it on the nail along with the hat and the scarf.

Ali's wife was furious and said, "He is taking advantage of our kindness. No, he is taking advantage of your weakness."

"But what can I do? We agreed that he could do whatever he wants with his nail. But fear not, he cannot put anything more on the nail," said Ali trying to assure his wife.

The next day, Nasruddin showed up again.

"Oh God, it's you again," shouted Ali, tugging furiously at his moustache.

"Yes," said Nasruddin with a sneer.

Ali tried to shut the door in his face, but Nasruddin had already placed his foot inside—nobody was going to stop him from worshipping his nail.

He entered, dragging behind him the carcass of a cow and proceeded to hang it on his nail.

Ali's wife screamed at her husband, "Get that out of my house or I am leaving!"

"Nasruddin, this is going too far," yelled Ali.

"But you signed the contract, good neighbour," replied Nasruddin, calmly.

"Well, we will see about that," said Ali. "Let the council of elders make a ruling."

Soon, an assembly of all the wise men in the village was called. Ali, fretting and fuming, explained how Nasruddin was troubling him week after week, all for a nail. Nasruddin presented the contract, without speaking a word in his defense.

The wise men studied it carefully. Finally, they decided that Nasruddin was right. He could do as he wished with his nail. There was nothing in the contract that said how the nail should be worshipped. The case was dismissed. Ali went home dejected. He had learnt his lesson.

After a sleepless night, he begged Nasruddin to buy his house back at an even cheaper price. Nasruddin agreed. Ali and his wife were only too happy to move out.

Mullah, thus, not only got back his house but was able to make a tidy profit out of the sale. He was a happy man now.